BIRDS,
FROGS,
AND
MOONLIGHT

ILLUSTRATED BY
VO-DINH

CALLIGRAPHY BY
KOSON OKAMURA

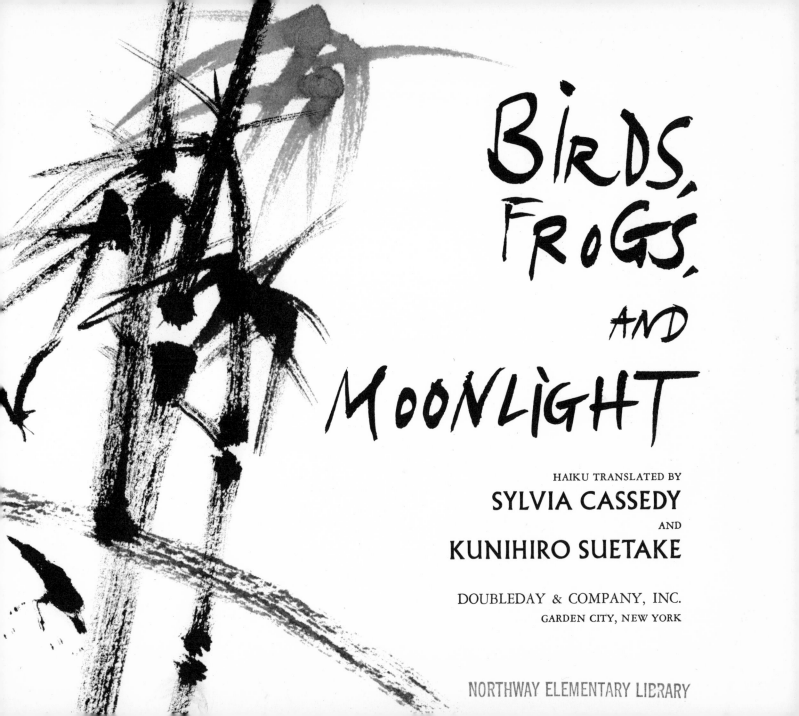

Birds, Frogs, and Moonlight

HAIKU TRANSLATED BY

SYLVIA CASSEDY

AND

KUNIHIRO SUETAKE

DOUBLEDAY & COMPANY, INC.
GARDEN CITY, NEW YORK

A NOTE ON HAIKU

Haiku (pronounced high-koo) is a very old form of poetry which originated in Japan some seven hundred years ago and developed over the years until, by the seventeenth century, it became fully absorbed into Japanese culture.

Unlike much of the poetry we read or recite or even write ourselves, haiku does not depend for its structure upon rhythm or rhyme. Instead, an essential characteristic of nearly every haiku is that it is composed of only seventeen syllables, divided into three lines. The first line contains five syllables, the second seven, and the last line five again. Of course, just as rhyme and rhythm do not transform every group of words into a poem, not every seventeen-syllable description can be called haiku. A genuine haiku captures a mood about a scene in nature in such a way that it creates a vivid response in the reader.

With so few syllables to work with, the haiku-poet must choose very carefully those words which best describe the picture he has in mind. A well-written haiku is very much like a Japanese brush-and-ink sketch where only a few strokes suggest a branch of cherry blossoms or a peasant ascending a road with his ox, and the viewer must fill in the details from his imagination. For this reason, reading haiku is as much an art as writing it. It is best to read haiku very slowly, letting each phrase suggest a new addition to the scene developing in your mind. You might return to it later for many further readings, as do Japanese students of haiku, bringing to it a new mood each time, and surrounding it with new details.

LIBRARY OF CONGRESS CATALOG CARD NUMBER 67-15373   COPYRIGHT © 1967 BY DOUBLEDAY & COMPANY, INC.
ALL RIGHTS RESERVED   PRINTED IN THE UNITED STATES OF AMERICA   FIRST EDITION

The English versions in this book are not exact translations of the original Japanese. The Japanese haiku writer uses word combinations that would sound strange and disconnected if translated word for word, and, of course, the seventeen-syllable structure would be impossible to preserve. So it was often necessary to add details in English that do not exist in the original, but which enlarged upon the imagery without actually changing it. For instance, the literal translation of the verse on page 21 is: "Old pond:/frog jump in/water-sound." The English version is expanded somewhat in detail, but the original image and mood are not significantly disturbed.

Of the haiku authors represented in this book, the two best known are Bashô and Issa. Bashô (1644–1694) was one of the earliest prominent haiku poets. The later years of his life were devoted almost entirely to religious contemplation, and it was during this period that much of his best haiku was written. Issa (1762–1826) seemed to have been pursued by tragedy all his life. His mother died when he was very small, and he was brought up by a harsh and unloving stepmother, so it is not surprising that a great deal of sadness was reflected in his poetry. He often wrote about small, helpless animals—lonely sparrows, undersized frogs, trembling insects—and took pity on them, remembering his own orphaned boyhood.

Perhaps you would like to try to compose haiku yourself. Choose a simple scene with only one or two subjects in it—an autumn leaf quivering at the end of a twig, or a group of birches casting pale shadows on the snow. When you have perfected your poem, and it contains just those words which best convey your mood, it will seem, as you reread it, like a gem suddenly breaking into hundreds of sparkling fragments of light when held against the sun. Sylvia Cassedy

The authors wish to thank Mr. S. Sugiyama and Miss T. Fukamachi for their help in the preparation of this book.

Alas, you cannot
scramble over the slipper—
poor, clumsy kitten.

KYOSHI

Surippa o koekanete iru koneko kana

スリッパを
越えかねてゐる
仔猫かな　虚子

Above the chorus,
listen! A single cricket
shakes a golden bell.

KYOSHI

Sono-naka ni kin-rei o furu mushi hitotsu

On the dewy trunk,
step by step, a cicada
gently picks his way.

KYOSHI

Tsuyu no miki shizukani semi no aruki-ori

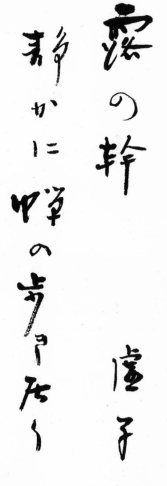

11

All at once, the storm!
Overcome, a poor sparrow
grasps a blade of grass.

BUSON

夕立や
草葉を掴む
薦村
村雀

Yûdachi ya kusaba o tukamu mura-suzume

High noon! A hot sun
bathes the town in quiet, and
stirs the sleeping dog.

HAJIME

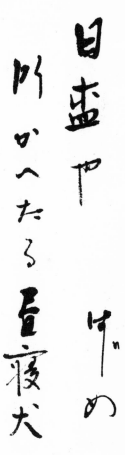

Hi zakari ya tokoro kaetaru hirune-inu

15

Little frog among
rain-shaken leaves, are you, too,
splashed with fresh, green paint?

GAKI

Aogaeru onore mo penki nuritate ka

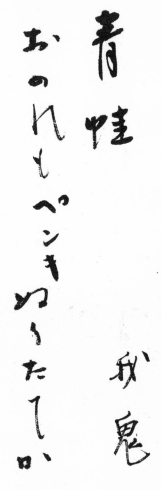

Lined up one by one
against the river current—
spider caravan.

SHIKI

Kawa kami e atama soroete mizusumashi

川上へ頭そろへて水馬　子規

Old pond, blackly still—
frog, plunging into water,
splinters silent air.

BASHÔ

Furu-ike ya kawazu tobi-komu mizu no oto

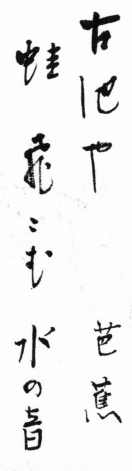

Red dragonfly on
my shoulder calls me his friend.
Autumn has arrived.

SÔSEKI

Kata ni kite hito-natsukashi ya aka-tombo

23

Now the pond is still,
and scattered water spiders
reunite at last.

AOHÔZUKI

Mizukumi no sareba yori-kuru mizusumashi

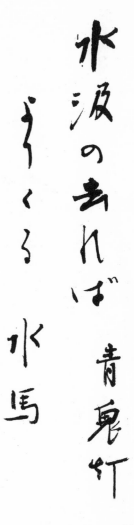

Look out, my sparrow!
Fly away! Fly away! See?
A pony trots by.

ISSA

雀の子 そこのけ そこのけ 御馬が通る 一茶

Suzume-no-ko sokonoke sokonoke ouma ga tôru

A discovery!
On my frog's smooth, green belly
there sits no button.

YAYÛ

Mitsuketari, kawazu ni heso no naki koto o

見つけたり　蛙に臍のなきことを　也有

29

Oh, don't strike the fly!

See? With knees bent and hands clasped

he prays for his life.

ISSA

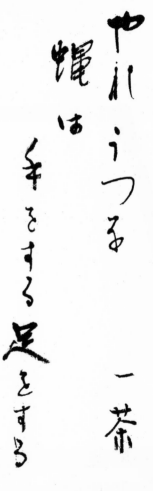

Yare utsu-na hae ga te o suru ashi o suru

Behind his long face

great thoughts stir. Astronomy,

perhaps? Foolish frog!

ISSA

Tenmon o kangae-gao no kwazu kana

Come and let us play—

you, a small, orphaned sparrow,

and I, another.

ISSA

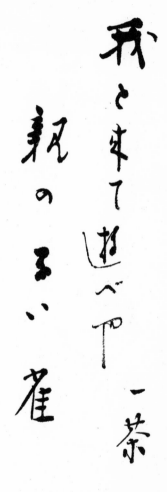

Ware to kite asobe-ya oya no nai suzume

In storm-tossed grassland,
one leaf, one praying mantis,
tremble together.

MIYOSHI

Kamakiri no sugareru kusa mo arashi kana

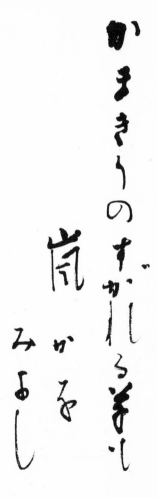

Butting, tumbling cat,

with whom do you fight? Ah, you

chase a butterfly.

KIKAKU

Neko-no-ko no kunzu hoguretsu kocho kana

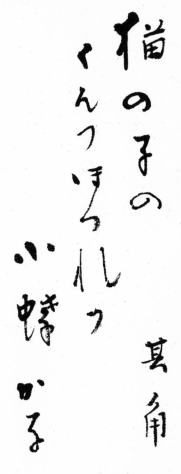

Detestable crow!

Today alone you please me—

black against the snow.

BASHÔ

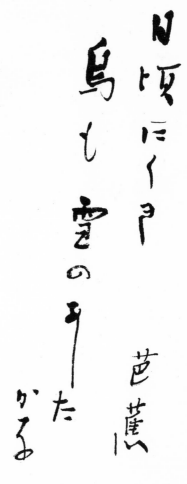

Higoro nikuki karasu mo yuki no ashita kana

Unbridled horse, leap
about the grassy hill; leap
to the autumn sky.

SÔSEKI

Kusa-yama ni uma hanachi keri aki no sora

草山に
馬放ち
けり
秋の空

漱石

43

Galloping pony—

alone, against the moonlight,

on a whitened beach.

KYORAI

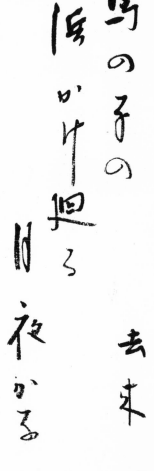

Uma-no-ko no hama kake-mawaru tsuki-yo kana

45

Leaping flying-fish!
dancing for me and my boat
as I sail for home.

KÔSON

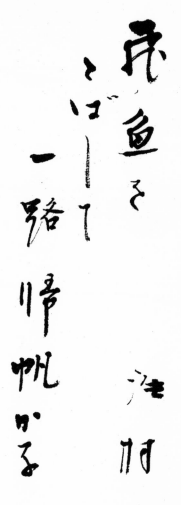

Higyo o tobashite ichiro kihan kana

47

Sylvia Cassedy is an author of picture books for children, most recently *Pierino and the Bell* and *Marzipan Day on Bridget Lane.* She was born in Brooklyn and attended the Ethical Culture School there. In high school, she won several poetry awards, one of them national. In 1951, she received her B.A. from Brooklyn College and later studied in the Department of Writing Seminars at Johns Hopkins University.

Mrs. Cassedy and her husband, an associate professor at the Polytechnic Institute of Brooklyn, have three children, Ellen, Steven and Amy. They live in Great Neck, Long Island, New York.

Kunihiro Suetake is a devoted student of haiku and has studied it for many years under Koson Okamura, the calligrapher of this book. In the year 1961-1962 he came to the United States from Japan as a visiting professor at the Polytechnic Institute of Brooklyn, and it was during that time that he and Mrs. Cassedy began collaboration on BIRDS, FROGS, AND MOONLIGHT.

Dr. Suetake, a professor at the Tokyo Institute of Technology, is a recognized authority in the field of electrical engineering. He lives in Tokyo with his wife and two teenage children, Hisako and Mikio.

Vo-Dinh is a full-time professional artist who has had nine one-man shows and numerous group shows here and abroad. His works hang in some of the most distinguished collections in this country. He was born and raised in Hue, the former imperial capital of Vietnam, and began painting as a child. He attended the Faculty of Letters at the Sorbonne and the Ecole Nationale Supérieure des Beaux-Arts of the University of Paris. BIRDS, FROGS, AND MOONLIGHT is the first book he has illustrated for children.

Vo-Dinh lives with his wife and young daughter in Matamoras, Pennsylvania.